The **Oldie**
BOOK OF CARTOONS

'Be careful, darling – it contains salt'

'I still think we should reword it'

The Oldie
BOOK OF CARTOONS

Chosen by
Harry Mount

This edition published by Oldie Publications Ltd in 2018

First published in 2018
by Oldie Publications Ltd

23 Great Titchfield Street, London W1W 7PA
www.theoldie.co.uk

ISBN-13: 978-1-901170-24-5

A catalogue record for this book
is available from the British Library

Printed in the UK by St Ives Group

Introduction

Looking through this heart-lifting selection of the best of *The Oldie*'s cartoons, you could be forgiven for thinking the cartoonist's life is a lucky, easy one.

What could be easier than drawing a small picture, with one – or possibly two – sentences below it? Nice, quick work if you can get it.

In fact, it's agonisingly hard labour. Journalists write. Illustrators draw. Cartoonists have to do both. And both picture and caption have to be funny. If either of them falls short, the whole cartoon falls down.

The result of all that tough graft, though, is pure joy: the most enjoyable part of the *Oldie* editor's job is going through the cartoons.

Every day, a dozen or so cartoons sail into my in-tray. And every day, I sift through them in search of golden comedy nuggets.

It certainly isn't hard work for me. When a cartoon works, the effect is instant. You don't have to second-guess yourself or ask around whether a cartoon works. It either does or it doesn't. And when it does, instant sunshine!

I'm deeply grateful to David Abberton, who has spent many hours, squirrelled away in the *Oldie* archives, mining for comic gold. As part of his studies, he conducted a scholarly investigation into the established themes of cartoons.

'The most obvious trope is the desert island but there are others,' David says, 'In no particular order, these are wife-hating; the grim reaper; aliens; cats; the guru on the mountain top; Mexicans; Heaven; mobiles and "How's My [insert theme]". There are honourable mentions for Munch's scream, giraffes, igloos and Excalibur (usually emerging from a lavatory).'

David picked out the funniest of these themes but was on the alert for completely original ideas, too, which abound between these covers.

Britain's greatest cartoonists are to be found here. It's a delight to have Ed McLachlan on the front cover, and on the pages that follow, too. An *Oldie* cartoonist of long standing, he had a memorable solo show at the Chris Beetles Gallery in St James's, London, in 2018.

All the cartoonists from the Great Oldie Toon Pantheon are listed in the roll of honour at the end of the book. I'm so grateful for their fine works in *The Oldie* – and for together creating the laugh-filled volume you have in your hands.

HARRY MOUNT,
Editor, *The Oldie*

'And you have two minutes on your chosen subject – the life and times of Christine Keeler'

'Don't you think you're a bit overdressed for a first date?'

'This is pretty much all they do now'

'We named him Xb32116, so we never forget the wi-fi password'

'We find the "naughty roof" more effective than the naughty step'

'Do you know from which filling the government is controlling your mind?'

'He's dressing me with his eyes again!'

'This lamp reminds me of my late
husband – because I hate it'

'Oh, yeah? Whom are you
calling pedantic?'

'You seem very content tonight, dear
– what's wrong?'

'General, I come to ask for your
son's hand in marriage'

'Tutankhamun wants to spell his name
with a P, like Ptolemy'

'Party like it's 99!'

9

'For my next slaying, I'll need a volunteer from the audience'

SHIRE CRICKET CLUB

'Do you fancy a glass of red?'

'Yeah, you're right – there's something in your eye'

'I'm sorry to be the one to tell you this, but you are a nut'

'You had better give that to me. He suffers from a paying-for-food allergy'

'And the dish was arrested and charged with historic offences related to a spoon'

'OK, you're in and you're in, and you're in... actually, you're all in'

'Ooh look – Timmy has sent his first letter from boarding school'

'And I'll huff and I'll puff and I'll tweet and I'll troll'

'I thought his new girlfriend was
called Deborah'

'Are you up for the ice-bucket challenge?'

'Yes, but Daddy may not feel like laughing when
he comes round from his operation'

'He took it with him'

SIT.

Pals

'They're toy-trainspotters'

'Miserable Sod and Stupid Cow, the therapist can see you now'

PLEASE LEAVE THE CASTLE VIA THE SHOP

'He's had nightmares over planning permission'

'I'll take it'

'I hope that's organic'

Pals

'We haven't seen you in church lately?'

'I can't give you a definite "yes" at this time but you are through to the next round'

'I'm afraid I can't discuss individual cases'

'You're always bringing up things that
happened a month ago! Why can't we let
bygones be bygones?'

'I thought we could freeze it . . .'

'Verb at the *end* of the sentence, Watkins'

'You have the right to remain silent . . .'

PARALYTIC GAMES

'Why can't you play with your mobile phone like any normal person?'

'We sat on that bench last year'

'Your mother and I think you are old enough now to tell us where we went wrong'

'The invitation says CASUAL DRESS, what's that?'

'He cashed in his pension'

'Surprise me'

AND FOR A BONUS POINT WHAT'S THE NAME OF HIS WIFE?

OOH, ER...

'What's wrong, darling? You're taking a long time to make a fool of yourself'

'That's the grande?'

'Now, don't lie to me. I'm not your wife'

'At this rate, all the decent wives will have been swapped already'

'Out, damned spot!'

'Frankly, I don't like this modern stuff'

'We're just couch potatoes'

'Jack, give me an A.'

'We don't know if it's a boy
or a girl yet. It can make
that decision for itself when
it's old enough'

'Elderly Abuse hotline? It's my 89-year-old mother
– her constant fault-finding is cruel and hurtful'

'Stop following me!'

K.J.Lamb

'Everything's set. We're just waiting for
HR to approve the risk assessment'

'...Semi-colon...'

'We must be some sort of gods'

'Your ladyship, his lordship instructs me to enquire
how long has this been going on?'

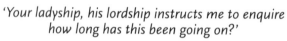

'Health and Safety insist on it'

'And remember – no snacking between snacks!'

'Honestly, Dad, they don't put little blue
packets of salt in any more'

'We should do this again some time,
except with different people'

'I'm not feeling the chemistry'

'This house has been in my family
for a long time'

K.J.Lamb

'The reptile house always gives me the creeps'

'I got six months, suspended'

'The kids have grown up and left, and so has my wife'

'Take me to your larder'

'We're still lost. I think we've been going around in circles'

'George Smiley, I presume'

'So – how's writing the self-help book going?'

CAREERS

K.J. Lamb

'You're not funny, Frobisher, and you're
not clever. Have you considered going
into politics or media?'

That bloke really got up my nose!

E.N.T. SPECIALIST

'They're a bit over the top'

'Where do I plug it in?'

'Some day all this will be yours'

'Have you got these in a funnier size?'

'I hate the word "boss". Just call me Your Dread Overlordship'

'And don't forget to act rich'

'Is this some kind of joke?'

'You've mastered the "Keep Calm" part.
Could we see some "Carry On?"'

'First Little Bo Peep loses her sheep. Then,
all of a sudden, Mary has a little lamb.
I say we bring her in for questioning.'

'My DNA was taken out of context'

'Extremely personal finance adviser'

'The High Street's regenerating – not so long ago these shops were all standing empty'

'You look terrible'

'Are we nearly there yet?'

'We're Holsteins – she's a Bechstein'

We're supposed to say
something funny

GED

36

'Are you sure this is what he meant by a cheap funeral?'

K.J.Lamb

'Good evening – I was in your area
and wondered if you'd thought about
installing an intruder alarm'

'You've got ten minutes left!'

'Actually, there's eight of us, but we don't count Sleazy'

'Now that your mother and I have your full attention...'

'Good news – you're not bipolar; you're French'

'I knew it wouldn't be long before you dragged my mother into it'

'Bloody caravans!'

'This evening? Hang on, I'll
check to see if I'm free'

'I bet that lot down at the Perfect
Match Escort Agency are having a
good old laugh right now'

'And don't try anything funny'

'Oh hello, luv... I didn't
hear you come in...'

'I didn't know L S Lowry had a son'

'I name this child Gatsby...'

'Yeah, well maybe Boogie Bear is clinging to me'

'The doctor will saw you now.'

'A good-looking man who achieved success in
everything he set out to do... his untimely death
was a comfort to us all'

It's another nuisance call from your mother'

'Don't we have a dress code?'

Lazy old git!

Eh? How many letters?

GED

Jonesy.

'Ugh! Disgusting...'

'You flay my back, I'll flay yours'

'Wait till your other dad gets home'

'This is a fine time to tell me our relationship is finally over, Fiona'

45

'The nurse doesn't come round very often'

'I always knew you would grow old gracefully, Eric, but I was rather hoping there would be one or two disgraceful highlights'

'I don't know her to talk to – only to talk about'

'I'd like to exchange him for a smaller size'

47

'I've just moved in next door, could
I borrow a cup of lager?'

'You're not half the man you used to be'

'Hello, darling. You have a visitor'

'They come down here to smoke.'

'As of now we're through – I want your hand out of there and never want to hear your voice again'

'You've got lots of good friends who'd be willing to risk assisting you if you decide to commit suicide'

'Now, where did I put those scissors?'

'And what do you do?'

'There's something pedestrian about it'

'They just love playing at hospitals!'

'Mary, if I tell you something about Roger that will sicken you
to the pit of your stomach, will you keep it to yourself?'

'I think we need to discuss
the human in the room'

'Lavinia! Don't tell me you've
been radicalised...'

'You're like a son to me, Tom – sullen, hostile, resentful'

'To be quite honest, I thought drag hunting meant something else.'

'What do you recommend to go with the others?'

FOR A FIVER !

IT'S A REALITY CHEQUE

'Tell me I'm not going mad, Doctor'

'I'm absolutely gutted, mate'

'They're wondering if the defendant would prefer heads or tails?'

'I like living on the edge. Why, just this morning I left my iPhone at home – on purpose'

'Lifer imitating art'

'Please God, Henry, not 'King of the Swingers' again...'

'Hi, I'm on the piss'

Jackson Pollock's latest masterpiece was ruined

'Pint of the usual, Vicar?'

'Can't you sex it up a bit?'

'You have reached your destination'

'Sorry, 007 – no machine guns
and no rocket launchers'

'He runs a tight, hollowed-out log'

'I'm going out... you may be some time!'

'I'm afraid we're going to have to let you go'

'I'm sexing up my confessions'

'Ah, Bob. Your next project – we want
you to clear your desk...'

'I'm leaving you, dear – I'll recommend
you to one of my friends'

'This piece is absolutely incredible! Where on earth did you get it?'

'For crying out loud, hurry up!'

'Say baa'

'How many glasses of wine a week?'

'So, apart from being the greatest mass
murderer in history, he wasn't
a very nice man either.'

'Look – a wild bore!'

'But doesn't the council object to you opening on Sundays?'

'Budgie jumping.'

'Outrageous! My Mensa subscription
has gone up by 13.74912 per cent.'

'Darling – they're playing our ringtone!'

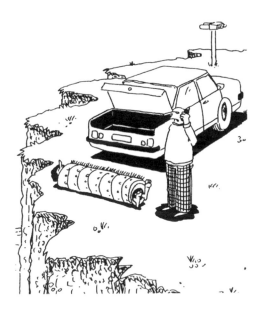

'You've caught us at a bad time.
Can I call you back?'

'Ladies and gentlemen of the jury,
does this man look capable of arson?'

'I've made a boob.'

'For heaven's sake, one glass won't do any harm'

'I've changed my mind. I DO want to be a burden, son.'

'The policy of diversity and social inclusion has really gone tits up'

'Graham, what's this in your cupboard?'

*'Another 500 quid ensures that the
pall-bearer look suitably mournful'*

'I've lost the plot, Miss Creswell, could you send it in, please?'

'Name? Rank? Phone number?'

Are you just going to sit there all day?

I'm in training for the old folks' home

'I sometimes feel I've outlived my uselessness'

'Do you think you'll ever get married again?'

'Very well, go back to pillaging.
Hengist can take over the raping.'

Hold it, lads, till he actually lights it up

'I want you to bring out my character'

'If only they'd had mobile phones...'

'Is there a reason my peas are
touching the mashed potatoes?'

'You rang, texted, emailed, Instagrammed, tweeted and Facetimed, M'Lord?'

'You work for the RSPB?
Well, stone the crows'

'I don't know much about rat,
but I know what I like'

Bookshop

'I'm not paying £9.99 for that! Who do they think we are? I've a good mind to write a letter of complaint to the publishers!'

'More O T, Vicar...?'

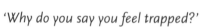

'Why do you say you feel trapped?'

BILL PROUD

'It's the worst case of identity theft
I've come across, Constable.'

.NAF.

'As a postulant, you will eschew
ostentatious clothing...'

'If you don't stop exaggerating,
I shall explode!'

K.J.Lamb

83

'No, George, I didn't speak.
That was yesterday.'

'Guys, this is Bob, my lifestyle guru'

'When did he start stroking a white Persian cat?'

'I knew that trial separation would
be a complete failure'

'Cut my hair... and the crap'

'I think we should start bickering, I don't
want people to think we're soulmates'

'We must be somewhere near the town centre'

'I'm not trying to start another argument. This is the same one'

'There's something of the
knight about him...'

'I'm on an alcohol-only diet
– I've lost two days already.'

BILL PROUD

GED

'Where do you see yourself
in five minutes' time?'

'Go to sleep, dear, or the childcare professionals will come and get you'

'You must agree to our privacy policy and terms of use before we continue'

FLEA MARKET

DOG

CAT

I've been
down in
the dumps

GED

'Sod off back to where you came from!'

'Well, I'm damn sure I heard a noise down here'

'This should open a few doors for you'

'Does my mum look big in this?'

'What can I do? They're a protected species'

'Sorry, Horatius, we won't need you after all for the bridge,
or Herminius or Lartius – we've got Obesius instead'

'Give it up, Bob. No man is an island'

'Come on, move! You haven't got all day'

'By God, if I was a hundred
and fifty years younger...'

'I like to think behind is the past and stretching
out in front of me is the future'

'OK, Who's going to be the look-out?'

'My wife takes forever to get ready'

'Have you tried sleeping the other way up?'

'Let's just enjoy our holiday. The whole incident with your stalker is over now. We won't see him again'

'I think we've spoilt it'

The new navigation app

'Son, I want you to go to that interview
and knock 'em dead'

'C'mon, Auguste, you must have some ideas for a sculpture?'

'We're never going to lure them onto the rocks with you looking like that'

'If you want a plastic bag for this,
I'm afraid we do charge'

'We'd like to start our Happy Hour, sir, if you'd please leave...'

'Not tonight – I have to crunch some numbers'

'Who's been eating my McPorridge with triple-choc fudge sauce, large fries and extra thick shake?'

'Behold, Ebenezer, I am the Spirit of Christmas Yet-to-Come!'

'Where would we all be if the meek
had inherited the earth?'

'Oh look, yours is taking a selfie!'

'Don't look now, but it's that ghastly couple who
were next to us at dinner last night'

'I'm the only deity this house requires'

'Course, all of this used to be ... erm ... more or less as it is now'

'Guilty of something, I can just tell'

'My door is always open, Dobson. Get on
to maintenance and tell them to fix it'

'No, you listen to me – like
everyone else on this bus'

'Chester, it's your night to feign interest in the children'

'Can we have one evening with friends without you banging on about religion?'

'I've lost my libido – have you seen it anywhere?'

'He's not a rescue dog, he's an alcoholic'

'Have you got anything that smells of success?'

'If you could tip me now, it would help
set the tone for the rest of the meal'

'Oh, a wise guy, huh?'

'Do you have this in a smaller size?'

'...and another thing – you don't have
wheelchair access!'

'I'm getting blackberries, chocolate and strong
hints of don't forget it's your turn to drive'

'Oh, no! I don't think old Rover's very well'

'Must dash – I've miles to go before I sleep'

'I've heard about this. It's called bed blocking'

'Could you hold this for a bit?
It says "Serve chilled"...'

'Tell me about these voices
you keep hearing'

'In my opinion they're a blot on the landscape!'

'And the area benefits from being
completely out of touch with
ordinary people's lives'

'Sonia! You'll never guess where I am...'

'Look, George, there's one'

'They seem to outgrow their iPods and
iPhones so quickly these days...'

'We're not living longer – we're living wider'

'I'm Napoleon, too. Wasn't Elba just awful?'

'Shouldn't you be at school?'

'We're agreed then. I'll put out some feelers'

'And they lived with the illusion
of happiness ever after'

'Decisions, decisions...'

'Had that Louis XVI in the back of my cart once'

'Have you swiped your Nectar card?'

'Excuse me – I believe that is my seat'

'All this effort just to get to Birmingham fifteen hours quicker'

'Oh, no, it's Ivan the Cerebral'

'We don't want your kind around here'

'Damn! I forgot the cheese.'

'Presenting... Mr Gladstone and his bag!'

SPACE RESEARCH INSTITUTE

MIND THE GIANT STEP FOR MANKIND

6 SINS OR LESS

123

'I'm not really gluten intolerant,
I just enjoy annoying people'

'I worry it weakens our defences,
but the men seem to love it'

'Ah. More properly you should have asked "Do
I have any idea with _whom_ I am speaking"'

'Another great thing about cruising the fjords – you're not likely to meet Somali pirates'

CAZ.

'Thanks for taking me out for a lovely meal
– fancy coming in for a pizza?'

'I'll go for the ants'

'Martha! How long has this been going on?'

'And how may I upset you?'

'That's the fire alarm'

'No, there's no one else here.
Except Stephen Fry, of course'

'I'm experimenting with an arrow that dramatically lowers expectations'

'Your Rolex is also a fake'

'Where the hell have you been? I was worried sick. I thought you'd been attacked'

'May I tell him why you're calling?'

'Far from being entitled to incapacity benefit, you seem uniquely qualified for a career on the high seas'

I've had more wives than I've had hot dinners. Neither of them could cook

Free range dinosaur eggs

'It's just... your father and I have decided
to live apart. From you, that is'

'Jeez, if you're going to cry about it, keep your stupid job'

'Tell me something about yourself that I wouldn't
already know from the internet'

'Gosh, is that the time?'

'I urge the jury not to wreck the life of
this young man, who has so recently
bought his first tie...'

133

'What would I recommend?
Well, Vesuvio's over the road is good'

'Our silences aren't awkward enough'

'That's not how we summon
the Prince of Darkness'

'That was Penelope. She's coming round for tea
and cakes and some thinly veiled barbs'

'The game's up – they've found the tunnel'

'Which tie do you want to wear –
spinach, chicken and gravy or oxtail soup?'

'My husband eats like a bird –
do you have any regurgitated insects?'

Cross dresser

'I'm going out to drum up some more business'

'It's bad news I'm afraid, Mr Hall. I've been having an affair with your wife'

you make drawing badly look easy

GED

'That pose is perfect, m'lord'

'What ever happened to
"You can't take it with you"?'

'Try and be a little less avant-garde, Mrs Groat'

Russell.

'I've found the mini-bar'

'I'm in a completely empty carriage.
Could you call me back?'

'Enjoy'

'New trousers, Sir? What chest size are we?'

'This old man – did he play "knick-knack" on other places besides your knee?'

'Excuse me. I just need to get some matches to keep my eyes open'

'Oops, missing you already'

'Is this one dead?'

'Hey, nice pad'

'I hope you don't mind, we started without you'

Have you seen my razor?

Are you having an affair?

GED

ORGANIC

IVES

MARK LEWIS O

'Sorry I'm late – I ran into some traffic on the way home'

Tony Husband

'We're so lucky being paid to do something we enjoy'

'Don't overdo it'

'There you go, Gentlemen: 2.8 units and 2.3 units. Please drink sensibly...'

'Hang on, that can't be right'

'His behaviour is too damned courteous
– I suspect he's been drinking'

'Hi. My name's Dave and I'm a compulsive rambler'

'I won't spoil your weekend, Higgins – come
and see me first thing Monday morning'

'I can't see the point of all these damn meetings'

'You could at least leer occasionally'

'Yeah, that's my husband'

'I'm surprised you got custody of us, Dad'

'One for the road rage?'

'I'm the token cretin to make the
others look like intellectuals'

'It's the inscription on Dad's tombstone. He won't let
Mum put "miserable, tight-fisted old bastard"'

'Don't worry, madam. I'll soon
get him down for you'

'...and may I please have a pillow?'

'Powerful sermon, Reverend'

HE'S ON THE OTHER
LINE – CAN HE RING
YOU BACK?

'Unaccustomed as I am to public squeaking'

'You never spray "I love you" any more'

'Living gods don't wear zip-up cardis'

'Oh, goody! Here comes the swede trolley!'

'Sure, he looks tough but
he can't hold his drink'

'Sorry I'm late. I overslept'

'You pays your money and you takes your Joyce'

'Mr Pontin! Have you been playing
tank battles again?'

'I think I'll wait for the paperback'

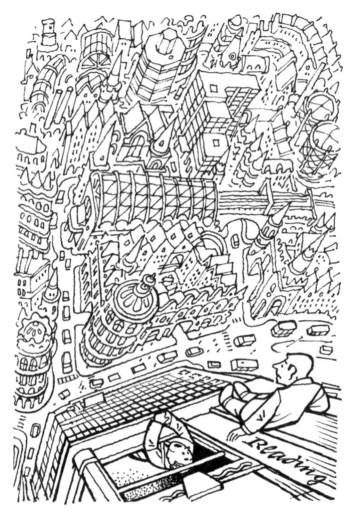

'But, Arthur, you could land in a very
unfashionable postal district'

'Sorry, the duck's off'

'We can't cure you, but we can try
to get you on Panorama if you like'

Glossary of cartoonists

Ace
AJ Smith
Andrew Birch
Andy McKay (NAF)
Appleton
(David Austin?) Austin/R1
B E Dawson
Philip Berkin
Stephen Hutchinson (Bernie)
Rupert Besley
Bill Abbott
Bill Huball
Bill Proud (BP)
Bill Round
Bill Stott
Bob Eckstein (bob)
Michel Cambon
Carol Stokes
Catherine Philips (Grizelda)
Cisner
Clive Collins
Cluff
Colin Wheeler
Colin Whittock
Crowden Satz (SATZ)
Darling
De la Nougererde
Drew Panckeri
Ed Mclachlan
Fran
Fransan
Ged Melling (GED)
Geoff Thompson
Geoff Waterhouse
GF
Gordon Gurvan (GG)
GPR
Grain

Gray Joliffe (Gray)
Ham Khan (Ham)
Holland
Martin Honeysett
Howard
Hunger
Huw Aaron
Inés
Inglis Thorurn (Inglis)
Ivor Healy (Ivor)
J Di Chiarro
Jelli Benn
Julian Mosedale (JM)
John Docherty (Jorodo)
John Lightbourne
Jones
Steven Jones (Jonesy)
Kathryn Lamb
Ken Pyne
Kieran Meehan
Tom Kleh
Lawly
Len
Paul Lowe
Mark Lewis
Dan Mcconnell
Meyrick Jones
Michael Corrigan (Mico)
Mike Turner
Mike Williams
Neil Bennett (NB)
Neil Dishington (Dish)
Nick Downes
Nik Scott
Norman Jung
Peter King (Pak)
Pals
Dave Parker

Pat Campbell
Paul Kales
Paul Lowe (Lowe)
Paul Wood
Paulson
Simon Pearsall
Phil Witte
Prock
R Lowe
Rains
Red
Rigby
Rob Murray
Robert Thompson
Roger Latham
Rolli Writes
Ron Morgan
Ronan Lefebvre (Sti)
Roy Jones
Roy Nixon
Royston Robertson (Royston)
Sally Artz
Samson
Sewell
Paul Shadbolt
Stewart
Term Larson
Terry Carter
Terry Mazurke
Theo
Tony Eden
Tony Husband
Waldorf
Warner
Wilbur Dawbarn (Wilbur)
Wilson
Wren
Woodcock